ISA's Instrument Technology Training Program is general in
nature. When maintaining any instruments in your plant,
be sure to follow the specific maintenance and safety procedures
provided by your facility and the equipment manufacturer.

D1383278

Electronic Test Equipment

ISBN 1-55617-358-X

Produced for ISA
by Industrial Training Corporation
Herndon, Virginia

ISA
67 Alexander Drive
P.O. Box 12277
Research Triangle Park, NC 27709
Tel 919-549-8411
Fax 919-549-8288

ISA wishes to acknowledge the cooperation of those manufacturers, suppliers, and publisher who granted
permission to reproduce material herein. The Society regrets any omission of credit that may have occurred
and will make such corrections in future editions.

Student Workbook

Contents

Using Your Training Program i

Overview and Prerequisites 1

Program Objectives 2

Segment 1 — Multimeters 3

Segment 2 — Multifunction Calibrators - Part 1 10

Segment 3 — Multifunction Calibrators - Part 2 15

Segment 4 — Function Generators and Frequency Counters 21

Answer Key 27

Glossary 29

Bibliography 33

Index 36

Electronic Test Equipment

Using Your Training Program

This is a comprehensive videotape/text training program. It may be used for independent self-study, or in a traditional classroom setting.

The videotapes are divided into segments, varying in length from four to six minutes.

This workbook is also divided into segments that generally correspond to the videotape segments.

Throughout the workbook, you will find symbols that will help you to identify how the information is organized:

Objective
Goal

Application
Doing
Hands-On

Self-Check
Review Questions
Pre/Post Test

Bibliography
Reference/Standard

**Calculator
Exercises
Computation**

**Concept/Idea
Understanding
Theory**

**Closer Look
More Information**

You may alternately view a segment of videotape and read the corresponding segment in your workbook. A variety of questions and practical exercises are provided to further your understanding of the subject.

If you are undertaking your training in a classroom setting, your instructor will administer a pretest and a post test during the course. Final evaluation of your progress through the training program will be based on a combination of test scores and observation of your performance during hands-on exercises.

Student Workbook

Overview

The training program, *Electronic Test Equipment*, explains the characteristics and operating principles of various kinds of test equipment used to calibrate electronic instruments and devices, such as controllers, transmitters, indicators, and power supplies. Guidelines describing the use of multimeters, multifunction calibrators, function generators, and frequency counters are provided. At the end of your study of *Electronic Test Equipment*, you should be able to perform the training objectives of the program.

Prerequisites

Electronic Test Equipment is designed for persons interested in basic instrumentation and control. Since this is an introductory program, there are no specific prerequisites for this study. However, it is recommended that students successfully complete the study of *Primary Calibration Standards* and *Pneumatic Test Equipment* in the ITTP/2 series. An understanding of basic physics and math will also be helpful .

Multimeters

1. Identify several electronic values and the instruments or devices associated with these values.
2. Describe safety procedures associated with the operation of electronic test devices.
3. Explain the functions of the controls on digital multimeters.
4. Measure electronic input values with a multimeter.

Multifunction Calibrators - Part 1

5. Explain the functions of the controls on multifunction calibrators.
6. Measure electronic output values to test instruments using multifunction calibrators.

Multifunction Calibrators - Part 2

7. Generate electronic output values to test instruments with multifunction calibrators.

Function Generators and Frequency Counters

8. Identify the switches, controls, and displays found on function generators.
9. Identify the switches, controls, and displays found on frequency counters.
10. Demonstrate how to generate specific frequencies, waveforms, and amplitude test signals with function generators, and monitor the frequencies and periods of the test signals.

Segment 1

Electronic test equipment may measure, supply, or simulate a precise electrical quantity to check the operation of electronic circuits. In most cases, test equipment can be categorized by the general function it performs. If it produces a precise value to an instrument under test, it serves as an input standard. As an output standard, it measures the output of an instrument under test. Sometimes test equipment is used to simulate the input of an instrument in order to verify the accuracy of the instrument's output. Selecting the appropriate electronic test equipment for each application helps to ensure the accurate testing and calibration of electronic instruments such as controllers, transmitters, and indicators.

Identify several electronic values and the instruments or devices associated with these values.

It is often necessary to measure a broad range of electrical quantities including voltage, current, resistance, frequency, and capacitance. Voltage is a measure of the electric potential of a circuit, and it is measured in volts or millivolts. Power supplies and thermocouples are typical examples of devices producing a voltage that may need to be checked for accuracy. Resistance is the opposition to the flow of electricity in a circuit. Resistance is typically measured in ohms and megohms. Resistance measurements can be used to determine whether continuity exists in a circuit or to verify correct resistance values. Current is the flow of electricity through a circuit. Current is measured in amperes, milliamps, and micro-amps. Multimeters are typically used to measure voltage, current, and resistance.

Frequency is the number of complete electrical cycles per second, and it is measured in hertz or megahertz. Frequency testing is a part of regular maintenance on instruments such as vortex shedders and turbine flowmeters. These instruments produce a frequency output that must be verified or replicated for troubleshooting or calibration. Frequency counters are routinely used as test equipment. Capacitance is the ability of a capacitor to collect and store an electrical charge. Capacity is measured in farads or microfarads. Capacitance testers are used to measure the capacitance of devices such as a capacitance level sensor.

Multimeters

Describe safety procedures associated with the operation of electronic test devices.

Because instrument designs and operating principles differ, it is essential to always follow facility guidelines and procedures for working on or near energized equipment. Even small amounts of electricity can kill or injure. Take the appropriate precautions when using any electronic test equipment. (1) *Be sure the equipment selected meets or exceeds the expected range of the instrument being tested.* (2) *Always follow the manufacturer's and your facility's procedures for testing any electrical or electronic instrumentation.* (3) *Check the condition of the components, including connection posts, adjustment knobs, the power cord and the power source before making any connections.* (4) *De-energize the instrument being tested before connecting the test equipment.* (5) *If it is necessary to work on energized circuits, be sure to follow your facility's safety procedures.*

The multimeter is one of the most widely used kinds of multifunction electronic test equipment for the measurement of voltage, current, and resistance. Multimeters can be either analog or digital. Analog multimeters include an indicator for displaying values, a function switch for selecting the electrical quantity to be measured, and jacks for connecting test leads. The black test lead is usually connected to the common, or negative jack, while the red test lead goes to the positive jack. These positions may change depending on the test equipment and the quantity and range being measured. Analog multimeters have a meter movement, usually a magnetic coil, as the sensor. An analog mechanical indicator displays the reading.

When measuring resistance with analog multimeters, the meter must be zeroed. Zeroing is necessary because the multimeter's internal batteries are furnishing the power for the circuit and batteries are subject to loss of power. To zero the meter, the range switch must be positioned at the appropriate ohms range. The black test lead is connected to the common, or negative jack, while the red test lead goes to the positive jack. The ends of the leads are connected together. Then, the Zero/Ohms adjustment is rotated until the pointer indicates 0 ohms. If the pointer cannot be properly adjusted, the batteries should be replaced. Once the pointer indicates 0 ohms, the shorted ends of the test leads can be disconnected.

Digital multimeters do not contain a meter movement. Consequently, mechanical adjustments, such as zeroing the meter, are not necessary. A digital display can provide precise numerical values and display the units of measurement. For this reason, digital displays can usually be read more precisely or accurately than analog displays.

Explain the functions of the controls on digital multimeters.

A multimeter has function switches to select the measurement, range switches to select the value of the measurement, and jacks for connecting color-coded test leads. The black test lead is usually connected to the common, or negative jack, while the red test lead goes to the positive jack. These positions may change depending on the test equipment and the quantity and range being measured. Some digital multimeters are designed to automatically select the proper range based on the signal being tested. This function is called auto ranging.

Always inspect the condition of any test equipment before using it. Look for signs of visible damage on the multimeter case and the leads, for example. If there are visible signs of damage, such as cracks, select another multimeter. Whenever possible, use the test leads provided for the meter. If it is not possible to use the leads furnished with the instrument, verify that the replacement leads match the current and voltage ratings of the multimeter. Before making or removing connections, de-energize the circuit being tested. After the test is completed, turn the meter off. Store the instrument and the leads properly.

General guidelines for inspection of analog multimeters include the following steps: (1) Examine the case, carefully. The integrity of the instrument's insulation is designed to protect the user from electrical shock while handling the equipment. (2) Look for any insulation damage such as cracks, chips, burns or deterioration that expose internal metal parts or reduce the spacing between the metal parts. (3) Examine the leads. Cuts, burned areas, deterioration, or other damage can adversely affect the insulation strength of the leads.

Make certain that the battery compartment cover is securely fastened in place before using the instrument. If it is necessary to remove the battery compartment cover, take time to verify that the proper fuses are being used. Often, fuses are located adjacent to the batteries. Whenever a fuse must be replaced, calibrate the instrument before returning it to service. Severe overloads may have damaged the circuitry of the instrument despite the protection that was afforded by the fuse. Use only the specified fuse types or replacement fuses. Information on the correct fuse types can be found in the manufacturer's replacement parts list.

The batteries that supply power for resistance measurements need to be replaced periodically. The manufacturer's service manual will describe the conditions that indicate when it is necessary to replace the batteries and specify the type of batteries required. Most manufacturers suggest that batteries should be replaced before their useful life has expired. Failure to do so may result in corrosion and battery leakage. To install or replace batteries, de-energize and disconnect the test leads from the instrument. The cover to externally accessible battery compartments is usually held by a single screw. Be sure to observe polarity when replacing the batteries.

Routine care of multimeters should include the following precautions. (1) Immediately clean all spilled materials and wipe the instrument dry. If the spillage is corrosive, neutralize the corrosive material with a suitable cleaner and remove the spillage. (2) Most multimeters have an Off/Transit position switch. Turn the switch to Off when the meter is not in use. (3) Avoid prolonged exposure or use in areas subject to extreme temperatures. (4) Conditions in which the instrument is exposed to extreme humidity, dust, corrosive fumes, strong electrical or electromagnetic interferences, vibration, or mechanical shock should be kept to a minimum whenever possible. (5) When the instrument is not in use, store it properly. If the instrument is to be stored more than 30 days, it is good practice to remove the batteries.

Multimeters

Measure electronic input values with a multimeter.

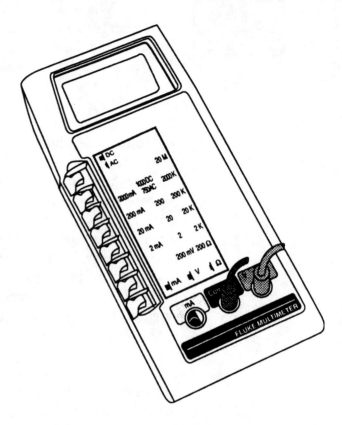

Multimeters can be used to check the resistance of a circuit. It is good practice to de-energize the circuit before making any connections to it. To ensure that only the appropriate resistance is being measured, isolate the component that is being tested from the rest of the circuit. In the example provided in this program, the function switch is positioned to ohms to set the meter to measure continuity. The range switch is set to 2 KΩ, and the resistance value is indicated on the display. Continuity is indicated by a low resistance value.

Exact resistance values of components, such as an R-F choke, may also be checked with a multimeter. Attach the test leads to the meter. Touch the leads together to check their resistance. Observe the display and note the value. Subtract this value from the component reading to get the actual value of the resistance. The manufacturer's literature for the component will indicate its expected resistance value. This information is necessary to determine the appropriate range switch. Set the multimeter's range switch to the expected resistance value of the component. Check the value of the resistance and compare it to the expected value. If the value is within the tolerance specified by the manufacturer, the component can be considered to be in proper working order.

Multimeters are frequently used to take voltage measurements. When multimeters are used to measure voltage, the meter's range and function switches should be set for the highest anticipated value. For this example, the output voltage of a DC power supply was measured and adjusted to 24 volts. Connect the black lead to the negative side of the power supply and the red lead to the positive side. The output voltage of the power supply will be indicated on the display. AC voltages are measured in a similar manner. Always verify that the function switches and range switches are properly positioned for the type and amount of voltage that is expected.

Multimeters are also used to measure current. The example used to illustrate current measurements measured a 4-20 mA DC output from a transducer. To prepare for the test, the black lead was connected to common. The red lead was connected to the milliamp terminal. However, many multimeters have separate jacks for current, so it is important to read the manufacturer's instructions when making connections. Next, the function and range switches must be selected for the quantity being measured.

Current measurements require the ammeter to be in series with the circuit; thus, the circuit must be de-energized in order to make the connections. *Coordinate with the appropriate plant personnel to ensure that all safety requirements are met before working on or de-energizing any installed process control instruments.* After the circuit is de-energized, the multimeter can be connected in series with the transducer. Verify that the red lead is connected to the positive side of the circuit and the black lead is connected to the negative side of the circuit. (Digital multimeters will show a negative reading if the series circuit is not connected properly. With analog multimeters, incorrect polarity causes the needle to drive against the peg, which could damage the meter.) Energize the circuit. The output current value will be indicated on the meter display. Turn the power to the circuit off before disconnecting the meter.

Multimeters

Hands-On Exercises

1. Become familiar with the types of test instruments routinely used in your facility. Identify which types of test instruments are designed to measure different types of electrical values.

2. Review the operating instructions and calibration guidelines for these instruments. Find out if your facility specifies that certain types of specialized test instruments be used in particular applications.

Review Questions

1. Identify three electrical values that are routinely measured with multimeters.
    a. _____
    b. _____
    c. _____

2. _____ - type multimeters contain a mechanical movement and must be zeroed before they are used to take a resistance measurement.

3. On most digital multimeters, the black test lead is usually connected to the _____ jack.

4. If it is not possible to use the leads furnished with a multimeter, it is essential that the ratings for the replacement leads match the _____ and _____ ratings for the meter.

5. Some digital multimeters have a function called _____ that automatically selects the proper range for the instrument being tested.

Segment 2

Testing and calibrating individual instruments and instrument loops is an important part of ensuring the proper operation of process control systems. The maintenance of a loop generally includes calibrating the individual instruments, verifying the output of the sensing elements, and checking the operation of the final control element. Although the individual calibrations can each be done accurately and efficiently with specialized test equipment, another option is available. Some instrument manufacturers' have consolidated several calibration and test functions into a single instrument that can accept and display a variety of input signals and generate and display a variety of output signals. Such multifunction calibrators make it possible to complete a wide variety of tasks with a single calibration device.

Explain the functions of the controls on multifunction calibrators.

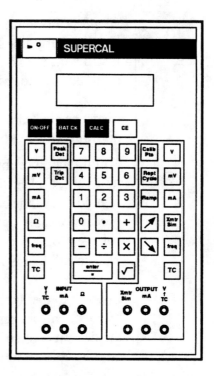

The liquid crystal display (LCD) indicates measurement information and prompting messages. Input information is indicated on the left side of the display. Output information is displayed on the right side.

The keypad is divided into three sections. The input function keys are on the left side of the pad. The output function keys are located on the right. The center of the pad is reserved for keying in input values and data manipulation. Consequently, the instrument can receive an input signal and provide an output signal simultaneously.

Terminals are located on the lower portion of the instrument. Input signals enter through the input terminals. Output signals leave the calibrator through the output terminals. The calibrator's input and output sections have entirely separate controls and indications.

Information on the use of the input section of multifunction calibrators is described in this segment. Information on the output section of the instrument is described in the following segment. Since the calibrator is portable, it should be noted that all of the calibrations shown at the bench in this training program can be done in the field.

As with most multifunction calibrators, the unit used as an example has a rechargeable battery. When the calibrator is turned on, the instrument does a self-calibration to verify its proper operation and, then, is ready for operation.

Measure electronic output values to test instruments using multifunction calibrators.

Multifunction calibrators can measure and indicate voltage, millivolts, milliamps, resistance, and frequency. The *Voltage* input function key is selected to measure a voltage, such as a 1-5 volt DC process variable signal. The test leads are first connected to the voltage input jacks on the calibrator and then to the circuit. The voltage will be displayed on the left side of the LCD.

In order to measure voltage in millivolts, the *Millivolt* function key is selected, and the test leads are connected to the millivolt circuit. In the field, it is often necessary to measure a 4-20 milliamp signal. To do this with a multifunction calibrator, the milliamp function is selected on the input section of the keypad, and the test leads are connected to the input milliamp terminals. The LCD indicates the function selected. Next, connect the instrument's leads to the P/I transducer circuit. The calibrator must be connected in series. Once this is done, power is applied, and the transducer's output signal is displayed on the LCD.

Measuring the resistance of resistance temperature detectors or RTDs is also often required. These are temperature-sensing devices that change resistance as temperature changes. To set the instrument to measure an RTD's resistance, the ohms function is selected on the input portion of the keypad and the leads are connected to the ohms terminals. Short the ends of the test leads together to determine their resistance. The resistance of the test leads is displayed on the LCD. This value must be subtracted from the reading of the RTD circuit's resistance to get a true value for the resistance. The calibrator used as an example has a built-in calculator function that can do this automatically.

With the RTD at a known temperature, the device is connected to the calibrator. The resistance of the circuit is displayed on the LCD. Using the built-in calculator function, the resistance of the test leads is subtracted from the RTD circuit resistance to obtain a true value. To verify the accuracy of the RTD, it is necessary to check the actual temperature of the RTD and look up the corresponding resistance in the RTD tables. This resistance is then compared to the measured resistance.

Multifunction calibrators can also measure frequency, using the same technique used to measure voltage. First, the frequency input function is selected, and the test leads are connected to the frequency input jacks. Then, the test leads are connected to the signal source. The frequency indication can be observed on the LCD.

These instruments can also measure a thermocouple's output EMF. Because the multifunction calibrator shown in this program has internal reference junction compensation, the actual temperature at the thermocouple's measuring junction can be displayed. The thermocouple input function is selected first. Then, the appropriate option for the type of thermocouple is chosen. Options 1 through 4 are provided. For this instrument, the types listed as standard options are the J type, the K type, the T type, and the E type, each of which has a different temperature range and voltage/temperature characteristics. The selection of the appropriate temperature scale is the last input setting required. Thermocouple wire should be used to make the test connections at the calibrator. This eliminates the creation of a second junction where the test leads are connected to the thermocouple. Proper polarity can be ensured by always connecting the red lead to the negative input voltage jack. The thermocouple positive lead is connected to the positive input voltage jack. The temperature at the thermocouple can then be read directly from the LCD.

Additional input functions on the calibrator used as an example are the *peak detect* function and the *trip detect* function. The peak detect function identifies the maximum value of the variable to be measured. Assume the variable is current. After selecting the variable mA, the peak detect function is pressed. This triggers a display that includes a character which identifies the calibrator as being in the peak detect mode, and the highest value measured. This function is exited by reselecting the same variable or any other. On this instrument, the peak detect mode operates on all input variables except frequency.

The trip detect function is generally used to calibrate voltage or current alarms. This function detects a resistance change across the calibrator's ohms input terminals. In order for the function to operate, the resistance change must exceed a certain value within a specified range. The keys that must be pressed to set up the function are the Ω key and the *Trip Detect* key. The display will then indicate whether the measured resistance is within the specified range or overrange. When a trip is detected, the display indicates that a trip has occurred. The *Trip Detect* key is pressed to reselect following a trip.

Most multifunction calibrators have AC-DC adaptor modules to measure AC or DC voltages up to approximately 500 volts. Adapter modules must be connected to the instruments precisely as indicated in the manufacturers' operating instructions. Often, toggle switches are used to select the type of voltage to be measured. In most cases, when taking high voltage measurements, a multiplier is used to obtain the correct voltage. High voltage measurements taken on the instrument used as an example are multiplied by 100 to obtain the correct value.

Hands-On Exercises

1. Become familiar with the types of multifunction calibrators routinely used in your facility. Compare their strengths and limitations.

2. Review the operating instructions and calibration guidelines for these instruments. Practice using the input section of a multifunction calibrator to measure and display electronic values.

Review Questions

1. True or False. Multifunction calibrators have entirely separate controls and indications for input and output sections.

2. Most multifunction calibrators do a _____ to verify that they are operating properly when they are turned on.

3. To measure a value with a multifunction calibrator, the _____ is used to select the appropriate electrical value.

4. Test leads are first connected to input jacks on the _____, and then to the instrument or circuit being tested.

5. The actual temperature at a thermocouple measuring junction can be displayed if the multifunction calibrator has _____.

Segment 3

The output section of multifunction calibrators is designed to generate and display a variety of output signals. Generally, the output section can supply most of the same types of signals that the input section accepts. These output signals include voltage, millivolts, milliamps, frequency, and signals from thermocouples. In addition, the output section has several special functions.

Generate electronic output values to test instruments with multifunction calibrators.

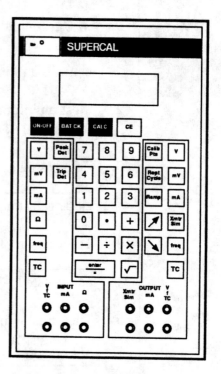

To supply a voltage signal, the connections must be made from the voltage output terminals to the device being tested. The example used for this exercise is an E/P transducer. After the connections are made, the *Voltage* output key is pressed. In response, the calibrator supplies a prompt for the value of the voltage. After the appropriate value is keyed in, the *Enter* key is pressed. The calibrator then provides the appropriate DC voltage output. To supply a millivolt test signal, the test leads are connected in the same manner as for voltage. However, the millivolt output function is selected. Then, the appropriate value for millivoltage is entered at the prompt.

Many control loops operate on a signal range of 4-20 milliamps. Often, it is necessary to supply precise milliamp values to calibrate the instruments in the loop. As with other voltage output functions, the test connections for the milliamp output function must be made before the calibrator's output signal is selected.

Generally, the low-end input value is checked first. For example, the first value keyed into the calibrator might be 05.6 mA. After the *Enter* key is pressed, the calibrator supplies a process signal equivalent to ten percent of the indicator's range. The value on the process variable display is observed, noted, and compared to the expected value. To check the high end of the range, a value equivalent to ninety percent might be keyed into the calibrator. In this example, the value is 18.4 mA. The process variable display indication should correspond to the expected ninety percent. Data points are recorded as each value is observed.

Multifunction calibrators can supply variable frequency square wave signals for the process instruments that generate or respond to frequency signals. First, frequency connections must be made from the frequency output terminals to the instrument being tested. Once this is done, the *Frequency* output function key is selected. In this instance, the calibrator's prompt demands the value of the peak-to-peak amplitude of the square wave. The appropriate voltage value is then entered. The next prompt demands the value of the desired output frequency in kilohertz. After this value has been entered, the frequency of the output signal begins to increase toward the desired value. The time required for the output to reach the desired frequency will vary depending on the calibrator's circuitry.

In addition to being able to measure the actual temperature of a thermocouple, the output section of multifunction calibrators can be used to calibrate a thermocouple transmitter. To calibrate a temperature instrument, the calibrator must be set up to simulate the specific type of instrument being tested. Assuming a type-K thermocouple instrument is being tested, the use of type K thermocouple wire eliminates the creation of a second reference junction.

With type K thermocouple wire, correct polarity is achieved by connecting the red lead to the negative output of the calibrator. The other thermocouple lead is connected to the calibrator's positive output. After the connections are made to the transmitter in a similar manner, power is applied to the calibrator. The thermocouple function is selected from the instrument's output section. After this is done, a prompt appears to select the appropriate key for the type of thermocouple being tested. The next prompt demands information on the desired temperature scale: degrees Centigrade or Fahrenheit. The final step for this series of actions is to select the temperature that is to be simulated. After this value has been entered, the calibrator sends a millivoltage signal to the transmitter that corresponds to the temperature and type of thermocouple that was selected.

In order to use the input section of the calibrator to monitor the output of the thermocouple transmitter, the equipment must be de-energized. For your protection and that of other personnel, always observe facility safety precautions when energizing or de-energizing equipment. Connect the output leads of the instrument being tested to the appropriate input terminals on the calibrator. The output of the transmitter used as an example is 4-20 mA, so the mA input terminals are appropriate. Once the connections are made, power is applied to the calibrator, and the mA input function key is selected. The milliamp indication appears on the left side of the LCD.

Often, calibration checks of instruments such as a thermocouple transmitter include five or more test points throughout the range of the transmitter. The output for each of the test points is checked to verify that it has an accurate and linear response over the entire range. The multifunction calibrator shown in this program has a *calibration points function* that provides the option of entering as many as 10 test points into memory. The test points can then be recalled, in sequence, and sent to the instrument being tested.

To use this special function, the *Calibration Points* function push button must be pushed. Then prompts will appear for each test point. For example, the LCD will prompt for the first test point, and the value of the temperature corresponding to the first test point is entered. In this application, the first entry is 120° C. The prompt for the second test point is displayed, and 160° C is entered. The process continues until all five test points have been entered. Since a five-point calibration check is being done on a transmitter with a range of 100-300 degrees, the instrument span is 200 degrees, and the test points are as follows:

10%	=	120° C
30%	=	160° C
50%	=	200° C
70%	=	240° C
90%	=	280° C

After each of the test points has been entered, the calibration check can be either manual or automatic. Pressing the up or down arrow keys enables the signals to be cycled through the calibrator and sent to the thermocouple transmitter. The transmitter's milliamp output is observed, noted, and compared to the expected milliamp output values. The calibrator also has a *repeat cycle* function that automatically cycles the calibrator through all of the test points. This calibration points feature can be used with all of the instrument's output functions except frequency. The interval that the calibrator allows itself between test points is approximately 10 seconds; however, the period required for the calculator to generate a frequency exceeds that time period.

Another special function that can be used with all output functions except frequency is the *ramp function*. To use the ramp function, the first step is to select an output function, such as V for volts. Then, the *Ramp* function push button is depressed. The calibrator responds with a prompt asking for a definition of the lower limit. Assume the desired ramp is from 1-5 volts. The entry "1 volt" is keyed in. The calibrator will determine and store the 1 volt value and issue another prompt. The upper limit, 5 volts, is then keyed into the calibrator. The calibrator then prompts for the time interval required. This is the time, in seconds, that the voltage output will take to go from the low limit (1 volt) to the high limit (5 volts) and, also, the number of voltage steps that the output voltage will increment as it goes from the low to the high limit.

For this instrument, the maximum value is 600 seconds or 600 increments. To improve the resolution of the function (approach a straight line), it is possible to either increase the time interval or decrease the voltage interval. *Arrow* keys are available to implement either of these solutions. Pressing the up arrow makes it possible to ramp from the low limit to the high limit and hold at the high limit. Pressing the down arrow makes it possible to ramp from the high limit to the low limit and hold at the low limit. It is also possible to continuously ramp from the low limit to the high limit with a 10-second hold at maximums and minimums by pressing the *Repeat* cycle push button.

It is also possible to simulate a two-wire transmitter connected in a process control loop using the special function called the *transmitter simulator*. In order for this function to operate, however, the loop must include a power source. The operating manual provided with multifunction calibrators provides tables for loop specifications and diagrams that illustrate the appropriate connections for the functions. After the appropriate connections have been made, the *Transmitter-Simulator* push button is pressed, and a prompt appears asking for the required value in milliamps. After the value is keyed in, the *Enter* key is pressed. The output of the calibrator then advances to the requested value. The transmitter-simulator function can be used in conjunction with the repeat cycle function. When this occurs, the prior entry automatically becomes the lower limit. Therefore, it is necessary to enter only the upper limit and the transition time for the ramp function to operate.

More sophisticated calibrations can also be done with multifunction calibrators. For example, by using the *RTD simulator function* in conjunction with the calibrator, it is possible to calibrate an RTD transmitter. This is done by plugging the simulator into the ohms input function to first calibrate the simulator to the zero and the span (maximum value) of the RTD resistance. Then, using a toggle switch, it is possible to transmit the zero and maximum value resistances to the RTD transmitter input. Illustrations showing the appropriate connections and specific keying instructions for these calibrations are provided by the instrument manufacturer.

Hands-On Exercises

1. Check the maintenance records for a process system that you are familiar with to determine if calibration checks are part of the scheduled preventive maintenance program.

2. Practice setting up a multifunction calibrator to do the types of accuracy checks and calibrations required for the instruments in the system.

Review Questions

1. To supply a voltage output signal, the connections are made from the _____ of the calibrator to the device being tested.

2. When checking the calibration of an instrument, the _____ end of the range is generally checked first.

3. True or False. The output section of a multifunction calibrator can usually supply most of the same types of signals that the input section accepts.

4. In order to use the input section of a multifunction calibrator to monitor the output of a thermocouple transmitter, the _____ of the transmitter are connected to the input terminals on the calibrator.

Segment 4

Function generators provide AC voltage signals of different frequencies and amplitudes, including sinusoidal, square, and triangular wave outputs. Some models may also have a frequency counter. Function generators may be used for instrument level and board level testing as well as component level testing. For example, a function generator may be used with an oscilloscope to measure a transmitter output or to provide controller input.

Identify the switches, controls, and displays found on function generators.

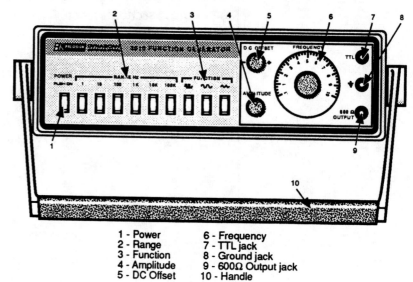

1 - Power	6 - Frequency
2 - Range	7 - TTL jack
3 - Function	8 - Ground jack
4 - Amplitude	9 - 600Ω Output jack
5 - DC Offset	10 - Handle

The controls found on most function generators include a power switch, an amplitude knob, a DC offset knob, a frequency control dial, a series of range selector switches, and a series of function selector switches. There are usually a minimum of three jacks: a transistor-transistor logic (TTL) jack, a 600-Ω jack, and a ground jack.

Range selector switches provide the relatively coarse frequency adjustment of an output signal. The switches found on the instrument used as an example are classified as decade-type switches. In practical terms, this means that each range is larger than the previous range by a factor of 10. There are six ranges, from one Hz to one hundred-thousand Hz.

Function selector switches determine the shape of the output waveform. On this instrument, three waveforms are available: a square wave, a sine wave, and a triangle wave. The *amplitude knob* controls the magnitude of the peak-to-peak voltage for the output waveform. The *DC offset knob* adds a positive or a negative component to the AC output waveform.

The addition of a positive or a negative component moves the AC waveform in the positive or the negative direction; that is, it changes the reference voltage about which the alternations are occurring. For example, assume a 2-volt peak-to-peak AC sine wave. If its reference voltage is zero volts, the positive peak occurs at +1 volt and the negative peak occurs at -1 volt. If a positive DC bias is added, the reference voltage can be increased to 1 volt DC. In that case, the positive peak would occur at +2 volts and the negative peak would occur at 0 volts.

The *frequency control dial* regulates the fine frequency adjustment of the output waveform. A continually variable control, the frequency control works in conjunction with the *step range selector switches* to determine the final output frequency of the waveform. To calculate the output frequency of a waveform, the dial setting is multiplied by the selected frequency range. For example, a dial setting of 4.25 multiplied by a range setting of 1 kilohertz results in an output frequency of 4,250 Hz.

The TTL jack is the connection point for a square wave output produced specifically for digital logic circuits. The *600-Ω jack* is the connection point for the output waveform. The final shape of the waveform is determined by the settings of the function selectors, the frequency controls, the DC offset control, and the amplitude control. The *ground jack* provides the common reference connection for both the TTL jack and the 600-Ω jack.

Frequency indication is usually provided by a frequency counter. Some multifunction calibrators have a built-in counter. If this is not the case, a frequency counter can be connected to the test circuit to obtain an accurate indication of the frequency or period of a test signal.

An individual cycle of any sine wave represents a finite amount of time. Assume two cycles of a sine wave that has a frequency of 2 Hz. Two cycles occur each second; therefore, one cycle must require one-half second. The time required to complete one cycle of a waveform is called the period of the wave. In this example, the period is one-half second. Each cycle of a waveform consists of two pulse shaped variations in voltage. The pulse that occurs during the time the voltage is positive is called the positive alternation. The pulse which occurs during the time when the voltage is negative is called the negative alternation. For a sine wave, the alternations are identical in size and shape and opposite in polarity. The period of a wave is inversely proportional to its frequency. Thus, the higher the frequency (that is, the greater the number of cycles), the shorter the period.

Identify the switches, controls, and displays found on frequency counters.

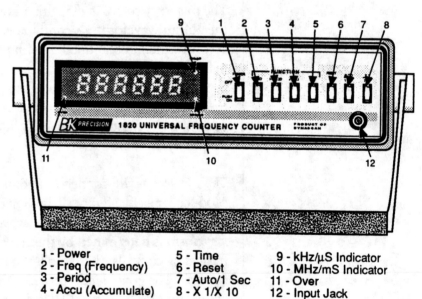

1 - Power	5 - Time	9 - kHz/µS Indicator
2 - Freq (Frequency)	6 - Reset	10 - MHz/mS Indicator
3 - Period	7 - Auto/1 Sec	11 - Over
4 - Accu (Accumulate)	8 - X 1/X 10	12 - Input Jack

The controls usually found on frequency counters include push buttons or keys for *power, frequency, period, attenuator control, reset,* and *time.* There are also *indicators* that show the units of measurement for frequency and period. One indicator lights when the measurement unit for frequency is kilohertz and the measurement unit for period is micro-seconds. Another indicator lights when the measurement unit for frequency is mega-hertz and the measurement unit for period is milli-seconds. The *Over* indicator flashes when the range of the display is exceeded. The *input jack* is usually a device such as a female BNC connector that is designed to accept an oscilloscope probe.

Depressing the *power* push button turns the unit on. Depressing it again and releasing it turns the unit off. The *frequency* push button selects the frequency-counting function of the counter. With this button depressed, the frequency of the test signal is displayed on the LED readout.

The *period* push button measures the period of one cycle of the test signal. The period of a waveform is a time measurement of the duration of one cycle. For example, the period of a 60-Hz waveform is 16.7 milliseconds.

The *x1/x10* push button controls the built-in attenuator in the counter. With the button extended, or pushed out, the signal is passed directly into the counter without any attenuation. Pushing in the button inserts an *x10* attenuator into the circuit. This attenuator reduces the amplitude of the test signal by a factor of 10 but has no effect on the frequency.

The *time* push button allows the counter to time the interval between two events. An external timing signal is usually required to enable and then disable the counter at the beginning and end of the interval.

The *accumulate* (ACCU) push button is depressed when it is desirable to determine the total number of cycles or events that occur during a specific time period. The operation of this control is similar to that of frequency except that the technician can control the duration of the time period.

The *reset* push button resets the numerical display to zero when the counter is operating in the *time* or *accumulate* function.

Demonstrate how to generate specific frequencies, waveforms, and amplitude test signals with function generators and monitor the frequencies and periods of the test signals.

Most function generators and counters can create and monitor a frequency input to an instrument. After the test equipment has been turned on, the next step is to select the desired waveform on the function generator. In the example used in this program, the waveform selected is a square wave.

The next step is to determine the desired frequency of the test signal. Assume the range of the instrument is 0-1000 Hz. The first input value supplied equals 10 percent of the range. Ten percent is equal to 100 Hz. The desired frequency range is selected by depressing the appropriate range switch. To produce a 100-Hz signal, the 100-Hz range switch is depressed.

The frequency control must be adjusted until the counter indicates a frequency of 100 Hz. The way in which the frequency is displayed varies from counter to counter. On the model used as an example, 100 Hz is displayed as 0.100 kHz. The function generator's frequency dial should be at about 1.0. The controller's display must be checked to verify that it is indicating 10 percent. This process is repeated until all of the remaining test points have been checked at their appropriate frequencies. Positive agreement with the standards established for the controller are needed to verify that it is operating properly.

Always follow facility guidelines and manufacturers' instructions when testing any process instruments because, although similar in appearance, operating principles and internal design may differ significantly.

Hands-On Exercises

1. Become familiar with the operating principles of the function generators and frequency counters used in your facility.

2. Practice setting up these instruments to do the types of testing required for the instruments in process systems with which you are familiar.

Review Questions

1. A _____ provides AC voltage signals of different frequencies and amplitudes.

2. The relatively coarse frequency adjustment of a function generator's output signal is controlled with _____ switches.

3. The TTL jack is the connection point for a _____ output for digital logic circuits.

4. The _____ control dial provides the fine frequency adjustment of the output waveform from a function generator.

Review Questions — Multimeters

1. Identify three electrical values that are routinely measured with multimeters.
    a. Current
    b. Voltage
    c. Resistance

2. Analog- type multimeters contain a mechanical movement and must be zeroed before they are used to take a resistance measurement.

3. On most digital multimeters, the black test lead is usually connected to the common or negative jack.

4. If it is not possible to use the leads furnished with a multimeter, it is essential that the ratings for the replacement leads match the current and voltage ratings for the meter.

5. Some digital multimeters have a function called auto ranging that automatically selects the proper range for the instrument being tested.

Review Questions — Multifunction Calibrators - Part 1

1. True. Multifunction calibrators have entirely separate controls and indications for input and output sections.

2. Most multifunction calibrators do a self-calibration to verify that they are operating properly when they are turned on.

3. To measure a value with a multifunction calibrator, the input function key is used to select the appropriate electrical value.

4. Test leads are first connected to input jacks on the calibrator, and then to the instrument or circuit being tested.

5. The actual temperature at a thermocouple measuring junction can be displayed if the multifunction calibrator has internal reference junction compensation.

Answer Key

Review Questions — Multifunction Calibrators - Part 2

1. To supply a voltage output signal, the connections are made from the output section of the calibrator to the device being tested.

2. When checking the calibration of an instrument, the low end of the range is generally checked first.

3. True. The output section of a multifunction calibrator can usually supply most of the same types of signals that the input section accepts.

4. In order to use the input section of a multifunction calibrator to monitor the output of a thermocouple transmitter, the output leads of the transmitter are connected to the input terminals on the calibrator.

Review Questions — Function Generators and Frequency Counters

1. A function generator provides AC voltage signals of different frequencies and amplitudes.

2. The relatively coarse frequency adjustment of a function generator's output signal is controlled with range selector switches.

3. The TTL jack is the connection point for a square wave output for digital logic circuits.

4. The frequency control dial provides the fine frequency adjustment of the output waveform from a function generator.

Glossary

Absolute pressure	1. The combined local pressure induced by some source and the atmospheric pressure at the location of the measurement. 2. Gage pressure plus barometric pressure in the same units.
Accuracy	In process instrumentation, degree of conformity of an indicated value to a recognized accepted standard value or ideal value.
Ambient temperature	The temperature of the air surrounding a particular location.
Ammeter	An instrument for determining the magnitude of an electric current.
Analog data	Data represented in a continuous form, as contrasted with digital data represented in a discrete, discontinuous form. Analog data are usually represented by means of physical variables, such as voltage, resistance, rotation, and so forth.
Analog	The representation of numerical quantities by means of physical variables, such as translation, rotation, voltage, or resistance; contrasted with digital. A waveform is analog if it is continuous and varies over an arbitrary range.
Calibration	Determination of the experimental relationship between the quantity being measured and the output of the device that measures it; where the quantity measured is obtained through a recognized standard of measurement.
Capacitance	The ability of a condensor to store a charge before the terminals reach a potential difference of one volt. The greater the capacitance, the greater the charge that can be stored.
Circuit	Any group of related electronic paths and components which electronic signals will pass to perform a specific function.
Cold junction	*See* **reference junction**
Current	The rate of flow of an electrical charge in an electrical circuit analogous to the rate of flow of water in a pipe.
Deadweight gage	A device used to generate accurate pressures for the purpose of calibrating pressure gages; freely balanced weights (dead weights) are loaded on a calibrated piston to give a static hydraulic pressure output.
Decade	A group or assembly of ten units, e.g., a counter that counts to ten in one column or a resistor box that inserts resistance quantities in multiple powers of 10.
Differential-pressure transmitter	Any of several transducers designed to measure the difference in pressure between two enclosed spaces, independent of their absolute pressures.

Glossary

Digital
1. Pertaining to data in the form of digits. Contrast with analog.
2. A method of measurement using precise quantities to measure variables.

Digital data
Data represented in discrete discontinuous form, as contrasted with analog data represented in continuous form. Digital data is usually represented by means of coded characters, for example, numbers, signs, symbols, and so forth.

Diode
A two-electrode electronic component containing merely an anode and a cathode.

Frequency
1. The number of cycles a periodic variable passes through per unit time. 2. Rate of signal oscillation in Hertz.

Hysteresis
1. A phenomenon demonstrated by materials that make their behavior a function of the history of the environment to which they have been subjected. Hysteresis is usually determined by subtracting the value of dead band from the maximum measured separation between upscale-going and downscale-going indications of the measured variable (during a full range traverse, unless otherwise specified) after transients have decayed. This measurement is sometimes called hysteresis error or hysteretic error. Some reversal of output may be expected for any reversal of input; this distinguishes hysteresis from dead band. 2. The tendency of an instrument to give a different output for a given input, depending on whether the input resulted from an increase or a decrease from the previous value.

Inclined-tube manometer
A glass-tube manometer having one leg inclined from the vertical to give more precise readings.

Jack
A connecting device to which a wire or wires of a circuit may be attached and which is arranged for the insertion of a plug.

Light-emitting diode (LED)
A semiconductor diode that emits visible or infrared light. Light from an LED is incoherent spontaneous emission, as distinct from the coherent stimulated emission produced by diode lasers and other types of lasers.

Manometer
A gage for measuring pressure or a pressure difference between two fluid chambers. A U-tube manometer consists of two legs, each containing a specific known gravity.

Meniscus
The concave or convex surface caused by surface tension at the top of a liquid column, as in a manometer tube.

Multimeter	*See* **volt-ohm-milliammeter**
NIST	National Institute of Standards and Technology, U.S. Department of Commerce (formerly, National Bureau of Standards).
Optical pressure transducer	Any of several devices that use optical methods to accurately measure the position of the sensitive element of the pressure transducer.
Parallax	The apparent difference in spatial relations when objects in different planes are viewed from different directions; in making instrument readings, for instance, parallax will cause an error in the observed value unless the observer's eye is directly in line with the pointer.
Primary instrument	An instrument that can be calibrated without reference to another instrument.
Range	1. For instrumentation, the set of values over which measurements can be made without changing the instrument's sensitivity. 2. The extent of a measuring, indicating, or recording scale. 3. The set of values that a quantity or function may assume. 4. The difference between the highest and lowest value that a quantity or function may assume.
Reference junction	1. That thermocouple junction which is at a known or reference temperature. 2. A device used with a thermocouple transducer which couples it to copper wires without introducing an error.
Resistance temperature detector (RTD)	A component of a resistance thermometer consisting of a material whose electrical resistance is a known function of temperature.
Resistance	The opposition to the flow of electricity in an electric circuit measured in ohms.
Sine wave	A waveform in which the value of wave parameters—such as voltage and current in certain alternating circuits—vary directly as the sine of another variable—such as time.
Span	1. The algebraic difference between the upper and lower range values. Thus, a temperature in the range of 20 °C to 250 °C has a span of 230 °C. See range. 2. The difference between maximum and minimum calibrated measurement values. Example: an instrument having a calibrated range of 20-120 has a span of 100.
Square wave	A wave in which the dependent variable assumes one fixed value for one-half of the wave period, then assumes a second fixed value for the other half, with negligible time of transition between the fixed values at each transition point.

Standard gage	A highly accurate gage used only as a reference standard for checking or calibrating working gages.
Test gage	A pressure gage specially built for test service or other types of work that require a high degree of accuracy and repeatability.
Thermocouple	A temperature measuring instrument that develops an electric voltage when heated because of the combined thermoelectric effect due to dissimilar composition between two electrically connected conductors (usually wires) and to temperature difference between the connection (hot junction) and the other end of the conductors (cold junction).
Thermocouple junction	*See* **thermojunction**
Thermojunction	Either of the two locations where the conductors of a thermocouple are in electrical contact; one, the measuring junction, is in thermal contact with the body whose temperature is being determined, and the other, the reference junction, is generally held at some known or controlled temperature.
Transducer	Any device or component that converts an input signal of one form to an output signal of another form — for instance, a piezoelectric transducer converts pressure waves into electrical signals, or vice versa.
TTL	Abbreviation for transistor/transistor logic, a type of digital circuitry.
Vacuum	A low-pressure gaseous environment having an absolute pressure lower than ambient atmospheric pressure.
Volt	A unit of electromotive force which when steadily applied to a conductor whose resistance is one ohm will produce a current of one ampere.
Volt-ohm-milliammeter	A test instrument having different ranges for measuring voltage, resistance, and current flow (in the milliampere range) in electrical or electronic circuits. Also known as a circuit analyzer, multimeter, multiple-purpose meter.
Well-type manometer	A type of double-leg glass-tube manometer in which one leg is substantially smaller than the other; the large-diameter leg acts as a reservoir whose liquid level does not change appreciably with changes in pressure.

ISA Publications

Application Concepts of Process Control. P. W. Murrill. Instrument Society of America, Research Triangle Park, NC. 1988.
(ISBN: 1-55617-171-4)

Automatic Tuning of PID Controllers. K. J. Astrom and T. Hagglund. Instrument Society of America, Research Triangle Park, NC. 1988.
(ISBN: 1-55617-081-5)

Electronic Controllers. L. M. Thompson. Instrument Society of America, Research Triangle Park, NC. 1989.
(ISBN: 1-555617-129-3)

Flow Measurement. D. W. Spitzer, ed. Instrument Society of America, Research Triangle Park, NC. 1991.
(ISBN: 1-555617-334-2)

Fundamentals of Flow Measurement. J. P. DeCarlo. Instrument Society of America, Research Triangle Park, NC. 1984.
(ISBN: 0-087664-627-5)

Fundamentals of Process Control Theory., 2nd ed. P. W. Murrill. Instrument Society of America, Research Triangle Park, NC. 1981.
(ISBN: 0-87664-507-4)

Industrial Flow Measurement, 2nd ed. D. W. Spitzer. Instrument Society of America, Research Triangle Park, NC. 1990.
(ISBN: 1-555617-243-5)

Industrial Pressure Measurement. D. R. Gillum. Instrument Society of America, Research Triangle Park, NC. 1982.
(ISBN: 0-87664-668-2)

Measurement and Control of Liquid Level. C. H. Cho. Instrument Society of America, Research Triangle Park, NC. 1982.
(ISBN: 0-87664-625-9)

Process Control Fundamentals Package. Instrument Society of America, Research Triangle Park, NC. 1987.
(ISBN: 1-55617-195-1)

Temperature Measurement in Industry. E. C. Magison. Instrument Society of America, Research Triangle Park, NC. 1990.
(ISBN: 1-55617-208-7)

Bibliography

Standards and Recommended Practices

The Comprehensive Dictionary of Instrumentation and Control. Instrument Society of America, Research Triangle Park, NC. (ISBN: 1-55617-125-0)

ANSI/ISA-S5.1, *Instrumentation Symbols and Identification.* Instrument Society of America, Research Triangle Park, NC. 1984. (ISBN: 0-87664-844-8)

ANSI/ISA-S5.4, *Instrument Loop Diagrams.* Instrument Society of America, Research Triangle Park, NC. 1976 (Revised 1989). (ISBN: 1-55617-227-3)

ANSI/ISA-S5.5, *Graphic Symbols for Process Displays.* Instrument Society of America, Research Triangle Park, NC. 1985 (Approved 1986). (ISBN: 0-87664-935-5)

ANSI/ISA-RP12.6, *Installation of Intrinsically Safe Instrument Systems in Hazardous (Classified) Locations.* Instrument Society of America, Research Triangle Park, NC. 1977 (Revised 1987). (ISBN: 1-55617-082-3)

RP42.1, *Nomenclature for Instrument Tube Fittings.* Instrument Society of America, Research Triangle Park, NC. 1982. (ISBN: 0-87664-9733-6)

RP60.9, *Piping Guide for Control Centers.* Instrument Society of America, Research Triangle Park, NC. 1981. (ISBN: 0-87664-556-2)

ANSI/ISA-S51.1, *Process Instrumentation Terminology.* Instrument Society of America, Research Triangle Park, NC. 1979. (ISBN: 0-87664-390-4)

Videotapes

Instrumentation Video Series. Instrument Society of America, Research Triangle Park, NC. 1985, 1986, 1987, 1988.

Continuous Process Control Series. Instrument Society of America, Research Triangle Park, NC. 1989.

Control Technology and Application Series. Instrument Society of America, Research Triangle Park, NC. 1988.

Industrial Measurement Series. Instrument Society of America, Research Triangle Park, NC. 1987.

INVOLVE ®
Interactive
Videodisc Instruction

Bibliography

Controller Tuning Series
Instrument Society of America, Research Triangle Park, NC. 1990.

Electronic Maintenance Series
Instrument Society of America, Research Triangle Park, NC. 1991.

Industrial Process Control Series
Instrument Society of America, Research Triangle Park, NC. 1991.

Interpreting Process Control Diagrams
Instrument Society of America, Research Triangle Park, NC. 1990.

Troubleshooting Series
Instrument Society of America, Research Triangle Park, NC. 1990.

Index

A

AC-DC adaptor module   13
Analog multimeter   4
Arrow keys   18
Attenuator   24
Auto ranging   5

B

Batteries   6
Battery compartment   5

C

Calculator function   12
Calibration   3, 10, 16, 17, 25
Capacitance   3
Capacitance tester   3
Continuity   7
Current   3, 5, 8
Current rating   5

D

DC bias   22
Deterioration   5
Digital multimeter   5

E

Electricity   4
Energized circuit   4

F

Field testing   11
Five-point calibration   17
Frequency
      3, 11, 12, 15, 16,
      18, 22, 23, 24
Frequency counter   3, 22
Function generator   21
Fuse   6

I

Incorrect polarity   8
Input signals   10, 11, 16, 17
Input standard   3
Inspection   5
Internal reference junction
      compensation   12

K

Keypad   10

L

Light emitting diode (LED)   24
Liquid crystal display (LCD)   10, 11

M

Meter movement   4
Multifunction calibrator   10
Multimeter   4, 7, 8
Multiplier   13

N

Negative alternation   23

O

Oscilloscope   21, 24
Output signals
      10, 11, 15, 16, 17
Output standard   3

P

Peak detect function   13
Period   22, 23
Polarity   12
Positive alternation   23
Power source   4

R

Ramp function   18
Range   4
Reference voltage   22
Repeat cycle function   18
Replacement fuse   6
Resistance   3, 7, 11, 12
Resistance temperature detector   12
RTD simulator function   19

S

Self-calibration   11
Sensor   4
Sine wave   22, 23
Square wave   16, 22, 25

Index

T

Temperature scale 17
Test equipment 3
Test leads 5, 6, 11, 15, 17
Thermocouple 12, 15, 16
Thermocouple wire 12, 16
Timing signal 24
Transmitter simulator 19
Triangle wave 22
Trip detect function 13

V

Voltage 3, 11, 15, 18, 23
Voltage rating 5

Z

Zeroing 4, 5